FLYING F...

WORLD WAR II after the Allied invasion of Europe and the mysterious Sergeant-pilot Fury had joined Z16, the special Hawker Typhoon Squadron to combat Germany's various secret weapons. Fury was a magnificent flyer, who defied death time and time again. He wore a strange Phoenix insignia on his white scarf and on his plane. Now, at a "forward" Allied airfield in Normandy....

Meanwhile, back at Fury's base in England Don Maltby, Fury's squadron leader was answering an emergency call from Air Commodore Murchison—

Sir, That would be difficult. He's not here. He took off half an hour ago, and we don't know where he is—

We're worried about fresh bomber losses over Germany. No, not from night-fighters. Deadly accuracy of ack-ack fire and blinding cloud penetration by searchlights. Let me speak to Fury.

Lancaster bombers headed for their target . . .

Target coming up in five minutes.

All okay. No night-fighters.

Switch on!

What! Searchlights that pierce clouds?

We should be out of range! How do they do it?

Next moment—

AAAAAH!

Two direct hits!

Now for the guns! The way is clear for the Lancs now.

Before Fury could return to Z16—

The news has just come through. A lone Tyohoon blasted the new anti-bomber menace at Ruhafen. It has to be your man—it has to be Fury! Well done!

Er, yes, sir. He, ah, must have got your message, somehow. Always quick off the mark is Fury, sir.

Don, how did Fury know? How did he anticipate last night's emergency phone call?

Look, he's back! We could ask him. But, on second thoughts, I'd rather not. Fury scares me.

Don't ask Fury about the message or anything. Let him make his report. The Air Commodore wants him to phone.

I've a hunch this isn't the end of the affair!

Next day, Squadron-Leader Don Maltby was driving with his adjutant...

What—maniac! Duck!

It's Fury! His Phoenix kite!

Fury's made it under the pylons! PHEWWWWW!

Wait till I see him. I'll throw the book at him. Risking lives and a plane!

Later—

I think you want to see me!

Too right I do! You nearly crashed us.

Sorry about that, sir. I was practising the kind of flying I'll have to do to wipe out the secret research centre for the enemy's manufacture of those infra-red searchlights and rocket-assisted ack-ack shells.

Next day—

The centre's underground—steel doors seal the entrance. A secret agent took the film. I received it from the Air Commodore yesterday.

No chance of destruction from above. Even armour-piercing bombs couldn't pierce the thick walls. The steel doors are the only possible weak link.

Fury had a job to get that load off the ground.

Special missiles—long range tanks. Not surprising. If it were anyone but Fury, I'd say he's unlikely to come back.

Over Germany now. It's going to get lively. Switch over tanks and jettison the spares.

At the secret research centre—

A raid! One was expected sooner or later.

No problem to us. We're too deep down. Close protective bulkheads!

All transports clear—

If the castle's destroyed it hardly matters. What's underneath can't be touched.

A full-scale reception. No wonder the job had to be solo.

KERPOWWW

The JU 88 made one pass . . .

Back at the Hawker Typhoon squadron.

He did it! Somehow, Fury wiped out the secret weapon research centre. News coming in now.

He has given his life. We know his Typhoon was destroyed.

Gave his life? I wonder! Fury is a strange one. If anyone can still turn up—

A breath of cold air.

I thought I heard my name mentioned.

Fury!

How!...

I managed to pick up a JU 88 over there. Gave me a tricky time passing over our coastal guns but otherwise no problem.

It's unbelievable!

I try to believe him but there's far more to it than that. Fury is like no one else in the world!

Oh, I don't know. I'm naturally lucky.

The End

14

THEN . . . 1931-32:—The Italian salvage ship "ARTIGLIO" took part in a spectacular operation to salvage over £1 million in gold from the P & O Liner "EGYPT" which had sunk in 400 ft. of water. A diving shell was used and the ship was moored in position by a system of buoys. Success at this depth in the open sea was thought to be impossible at this time . . .

THEN... AND NOW

NOW A modern diving support/salvage ship operates at depths of over 300 meters. It has a special propulsion control which lays 4 anchors to put the ship exactly over the diving position.

It has a diving bell, 2 decompression chambers, a 30-ton hydraulic crane and sophisticated diving gear. It also has a fire-fighting capacity with 4 water guns mounted on 2 levels on forward gantry.

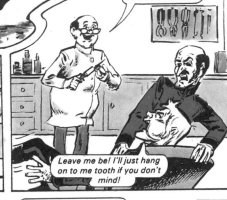

TOMAHAWK

THE CURTISS P-40

FROM the beginning of the Second World War to the close, on almost every operational airfield, you would find some version of the Curtiss P-40 on duty. The Tomahawk, and later the Kittyhawk, was heavy and slow compared to its main opponents, the German Me109 and the Japanese "Zero" fighter, but the P-40 had one big advantage. "It's the strongest ship in the world," said one American pilot, "and it'll out-dive the Japs every time!"

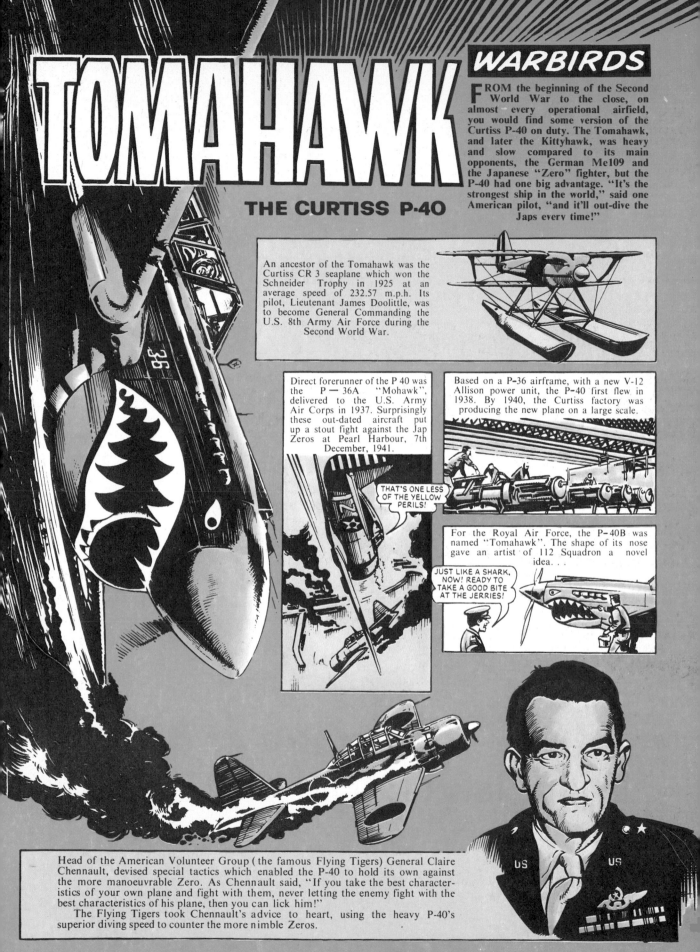

An ancestor of the Tomahawk was the Curtiss CR 3 seaplane which won the Schneider Trophy in 1925 at an average speed of 232.57 m.p.h. Its pilot, Lieutenant James Doolittle, was to become General Commanding the U.S. 8th Army Air Force during the Second World War.

Direct forerunner of the P 40 was the P — 36A "Mohawk", delivered to the U.S. Army Air Corps in 1937. Surprisingly these out-dated aircraft put up a stout fight against the Jap Zeros at Pearl Harbour, 7th December, 1941.

THAT'S ONE LESS OF THE YELLOW PERILS!

Based on a P-36 airframe, with a new V-12 Allison power unit, the P-40 first flew in 1938. By 1940, the Curtiss factory was producing the new plane on a large scale.

For the Royal Air Force, the P-40B was named "Tomahawk". The shape of its nose gave an artist of 112 Squadron a novel idea . . .

JUST LIKE A SHARK, NOW! READY TO TAKE A GOOD BITE AT THE JERRIES!

Head of the American Volunteer Group (the famous Flying Tigers) General Claire Chennault, devised special tactics which enabled the P-40 to hold its own against the more manoeuvrable Zero. As Chennault said, "If you take the best characteristics of your own plane and fight with them, never letting the enemy fight with the best characteristics of his plane, then you can lick him!"

The Flying Tigers took Chennault's advice to heart, using the heavy P-40's superior diving speed to counter the more nimble Zeros.

The Tomahawks proved willing workhorses for the R.A.F. in the Western Desert during 1941. They had to be tough, as some of the veteran squadrons had just changed over from fixed under-carriage Gladiators . . .

HERE COMES ANOTHER BRIGHT BOY WHO FORGOT TO LOWER HIS UNDERCART!

With wheels down, the P-40's under-carriage was extremely strong. One day, when a Tomahawk was forced down in the desert near the German lines . . .

DON'T LAND, SKIPPER! THE GROUND'S TOO ROUGH!

But Squadron Leader Bobby Gibbes, D.S.O., D.F.C., and bar, persisted.

COME ON! ROOM FOR ONE MORE INSIDE!

PHEW! WE'RE AIRBORNE!

And the gallant Tomahawk brought both pilots safely home—though they had to land "wheels-up" due to a burst tyre.

One man who used the "War Hatchet" to its best advantage was Clive "Killer" Caldwell, D.S.O., D.F.C. and 2 bars, Polish Cross of Honour. As commander of 112 Squadron he became the first Allied fighter pilot to shoot down five enemy machines in one mission. At the same time, he achieved another distinction . . .

HOW ABOUT THAT? TWO STUKAS WITH ONE BURST!

CURTISS P-40   MAX SPEED 352 M.P.H AT 15,000 FEET

REAR VIEW WINDOW CUT OUT

REAR VIEW MIRROR

RING SIGHT

VEE-12 ALLISON 1,090 H.P. ENGINE

SYNCHRONISED BROWNING ·5 INCH GUNS IN FAIRINGS

PITOT TUBE

SUPERCHARGER AIR INTAKE

SPINNER

RETRACTABLE TAILWHEEL

AMMUNITION BAYS STBD. WING GUNS

EXHAUST STACKS

PROPELLER PITCH CHANGING MECHANISM

0·3 INCH WING GUNS

CONTROLLABLE COOLER GILLS

OIL RADIATOR

REARWARDS RETRACTING WHEELS TURN THROUGH 90° TO LIE FLAT IN WHEEL WELL

STARBOARD RADIATOR

By January 1942, units of the Desert Air Force began to receive the new P-40 E machines. They became familiar to the R.A.F. as "Kittyhawks". The new plane could carry a bomb load of up to 700 lb.—and was effective against Rommel's Africa Korps in the Western Desert.

Because of poor forward vision on the ground, the pilots of Kittyhawks had to be guided to their take-off point.

In 1942, a new "Hawk" appeared. Known as "Warhawk", the P 40 F was longer than the previous model, with an American built Rolls Royce Merlin engine to give it extra altitude. These planes were the first P 40's to operate from aircraft carriers, during the invasion of French North Africa.

In the Aleutian Islands, extending from Alaska, P-40's kept guard against the Japanese menace. So cold were the conditions that the aircraft engines had to be kept covered by heated tents.

In April 1943, P-40's of the U.S. 51st Group in Burma successfully flew with 1000 lb. bombs to destroy vital bridges on the Japanese supply lines.

Throughout the war, constant improvements were made to the faithful P-40. Altogether over 14,000 aircraft were delivered during its six year production span. Shown is almost the ultimate P-40—the XP-40Q which could reach 422 m.p.h. It never flew in action but its slower "Kittyhawk" cousins continued to give yeoman service to their pilots in all the Allied Air Forces until the end of the war.

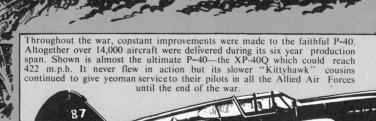

FIRSTS IN SPORT

How would you like to have been the man to take the first penalty kick ever awarded in football? That was the lot of James McCluggage of Royal Albert F.C., on January 6th 1891 at Old Mavisbank. Under a new rule, his team were awarded a penalty 15 minutes after the start of their Charity Cup Final against Airdrie. To his credit James scored from the spot.

Dr Roger Bannister, C.B.E., was the first man to run a mile in under four minutes. 3 minutes 59.4 seconds was the historic time he recorded on the Iffley Road track, Oxford, at 6.10 p.m. on 6th May, 1954.

The first international cross-country race took place on 20th March, 1898. It was run over a 9 miles 20 yard course starting from Ville D'Avrey, outside Paris, and was between England and France. England won. The first International Cross-Country Championship took place at Hamilton Park Racecourse, Glasgow, on 24th March, 1903.

The earliest international golf match was played on Leith Links in 1657 between James, Duke of York, and John Paterson, representing Scotland against two English peers. Scotland won. The earliest mention of golf occurs in March 1457.

The record for the Pancake Race, held annually on Shrove Tuesday at Olney, Buckinghamshire, is 63 seconds, set by seventeen-year-old Janet Bunker, on 7th February, 1967. This race was first mentioned in 1445.

The first two men to row the Atlantic were George Harbo and Frank Samuelson, two Americans of Norwegian descent. They left Manhattan Island, New York, on 6th June, 1896, and landed at St Mary's, Isles of Scilly, on 1st August, 1896. Their boat, the Richard K. Fox, was an 18-foot long, clinker built double ender with a 5-foot beam. It carried no mast or sails but 5 pairs of oars were put aboard.

The greatest height at which ten pin bowls has been played is 25,000 feet. On 7th January, 1964, Dick Weber played Sylvia Wene aboard a Boeing 707 "Starstream Astrojet" flying at this altitude.

On 30th June, 1899, Charles Murphy became the first man to cycle at 60 m.p.h. Using a specially prepared length of railway track and a heavy train as pacer, Murphy did a mile in 57.8 seconds. The engine shut off steam and Murphy bumped against the train. Officials grabbed him and his bicycle just in time and pulled them aboard.

The End.

23

ANDY MURPHY was the striker for Clinton United, the First Division Club managed by his brother, Joe. Among the critics of Andy's unorthodox style of play was Mr Hagley, the United chairman. Andy only went all out for about a minute at a time, and he was absolutely devastating. Hagley thought a footballer should run about for all the ninety minutes.

ONE MINUTE MURPHY

You were a bit too quick with that tackle, mate!

It's there! GOAL!

That was one of Andy's smartest goals! And if Dassan men think it was a fluke, we don't need them as sponsors! They don't know any more about football than Hagley does!

The game ended with the United winners by 2-0.

I'm from the 'Daily Spotter', gents. Is it true Dassan is going to sponsor the United?

We should want some changes made before we did. It is not settled yet. We are also interested in Branford City. We must see them play.

Changes! That probably means a new striker in place of your lay-about brother, Murphy!

We're playing Branford City at home next week in the County Cup. Should be an interesting match, eh!

The day of the Branford game.

The Dassan people are going to watch both teams today. This is your brother's last chance, Murphy. If he fails to impress them, he's out. Where is he?

He'll be here, Mr Hagley. He drives himself in to home games.

For the rest of the game, Andy did nothing.

Look at that, Murphy! Your brother isn't bothering and we are attacking! He should be dashing about chasing the ball! He's idle! I'll get rid of him, you'll see.

Andy knows what he's doing! I never try to alter his playing style.

That shot is sliced and it's coming across the goal—

The ball's going behind for a goal kick—

THE END

SPRING-HEELED JACK

Jackson, get those Limehouse reports written up! Move—look alive, man!

Ye-es, Sergeant Drew. Right away, Sergeant.

JOHN JACKSON was the timid civilian clerk at Ravell Row police station in the foggy heart of Victorian London. But Jackson had a secret identity . . . he was Spring-Heeled Jack, relentless enemy of all evil-doers . . .

Three murders in the Chinese quarter—two people missing. I want to know what's going on.

The people there are too scared to speak.

It's to do with the tongs . . . Chinese secret societies. I think . . .

Don't think! I want facts! That's why I'm sending out a patrol.

It's all right for the sergeant in the station! He's safe.

We could get ourselves killed going into Limehouse.

Jackson locked his garret door . . .

Quick, open the secret cupboard. I can help the patrol once I become Spring-Heeled Jack.

Helmet, suit and claw gauntlets were put on.

I suspect a tong war... bloodshed between murderous societies. The ordinary Chinese traders terrorised and forced to pay up...

I must get there before the patrol. Tongs seldom menace police... but you never know!

Chinatown! Good and bad but what a mixture! Hidden opium dens and gambling rooms, laundries, little shops and restaurants...

We'll learn nothing.

They vanish when we even draw near.

There's the patrol! I'll keep an eye on them.

Meanwhile...

You pay your dues to the Black Dragon... or die!

I am honourable man. No! Even if death comes like night.

34

35

You are spirit of good. I will be safe with you?

Come on!

Friends are outside. Go with them. I leave you in safe hands.

What the devil? Is it Spring-Heeled Jack?

No one's sure what I am.

A good spirit. He saved my life!

We daren't mention this to the Sergeant. He'd think we'd gone mad!

They'll bring Li Yen back here for his own safety. I must change back.

Jackson, wake up! Come down here, man! I need you to write statements . . .

Poor Jackson! Drew tramples all over him.

War between the Black Dragon and Flame Tiger Tongs causes terror. They bring in opium, run gambling dens and force us to pay them protection money.

38

(Continued on Page 97)

CAST, HOOK and STRIKE

JOE DODDS, a young English boy, lived with his grandfather, Ernie Dodds, in Australia. In partnership with an Australian called Merve, they operated a haulage business which had been left to Ernie by an old war-time mate. Some of the trips they made took weeks rather than days!

Phew! It's nearly two weeks since we left Adelaide with this perishing generator—I'll be glad to see the back of it.

It ain't any good grumbling—we'll be a few more days yet before we reach Wyndham.

Cheer up, Joe! Won't be long before we get to Derby—meanwhile, let's stretch our legs.

I'll jog a couple of miles and then take over the driving and let Ernie have a rest.

Later . . .

Hello, what have we got here, Merve?

Looks like the bridge over the Fitzroy River is out. Just our rotten luck!

43

Next morning—

Soon . . .

Up ahead, the crooks had reached their destination . . .

The End

48

MEDIC MULDOON

Muldoon, I trust I have impressed on you that my orderlies are not supposed to slip away on combat patrol with the Sikhs.

EARLY in 1944 on the Arakan Front in Burma . . . Major Parkin, officer commanding No. 31 Field Hospital, had his own way of discouraging the warlike ambitions of Private Muldoon, that reluctant medical orderly eager to become a fighting soldier . . .

Yessir . . . urgh, I'm duly impressed!

Tiddim Tojo's at it again! Better take cover, sir!

Muldoon, I appear to have caught a shell splinter in that part of me upon which I sit!

Tut! Tut! What rotten luck, sir!

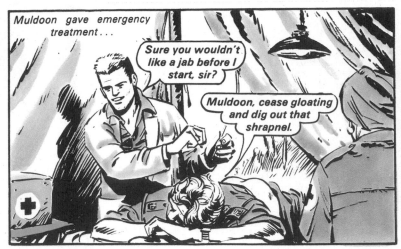

Muldoon gave emergency treatment...

Sure you wouldn't like a jab before I start, sir?

Muldoon, cease gloating and dig out that shrapnel.

Aaargh! You butter-fingered baboon!

Major Parkin was evacuated...

Sir, you can't disobey a direct order from Head-quarters.

Muldoon, there will be trouble should I learn it was you who notified those idiots of my wound!

That must be my relief. I am told he is a competent surgeon, at least!

Muldoon, meet Captain Gurung of the Indian Medical Service!

This is one for the book! A Gurkha with headlamps!

Muldoon, I suppose you are thinking that while the cat's away the mice can play.

Who, me, sir? Ain't you got no trust?

Just watch it, Muldoon! I'll be back!

Muldoon drove his new C.O. towards 31 Field Hospital . . .

Do you always drive so slowly, soldier?

Only when I'm on a dusty track covered by a Jap gun spotter, sir!

A Gurkha does not allow an enemy to dictate his progress. Put your foot down!

If you say so, sir!

Muldoon raised dust . . .

See what I mean, sir! Shall I slow down now?

Gurkhas do not allow shells to slow them down. You will continue at speed!

We've got a right one here! He's either got nerves of steel or he's a nutcase!

Have to pay a call on the Sikhs, sir! That crate of medical stores is for them.

You have my permission!

53

It is Muldoon.

Look what is with him! An owl clad as a Gurkha!

The antics of those sons of the lion rouses my medical curiosity.

Attention, havildar! Let me see some respect for an officer-sahib!

Sir!

Sir, that is castor oil!

That yellowing of the eyes could denote the onset of fever, Private Muldoon. We have a remedy in our medical box—that big bottle on top!

It is good for many ills, Muldoon! Spoon a dose into each of these brave fellows!

Muldoon handed out the medicine...

How about the patrol, Havildar?

We go this night, Muldoon. Lieutenant Ishar Singh agrees with your location of the Jap gun spotter.

URHHHHHH!

Muldoon and Captain Gurung drove away from some unhappy Sikhs...

Do I speed, sir?

Most certainly you speed, Muldoon! You drive a Gurkha!

Muldoon, why is not something done about that annoying shellfire?

The Japs use 70 mm. howitzers light enough to be pulled out to new positions before we can bring down counter-fire. Our only chance is to wipe out the observation post that directs them!

3 FD
HOS-IMS

A definite nutcase!

Casualties coming in, sir! Lieutenant Khan is on theatre duty!

We shall scrub up and join him. Major Parkin recommended you as a good theatre orderly, Muldoon!

Later...

This four-eyed Gurkha may be a bit of a nutter, but he's also a top doc!

That night...

Wotcher, Corporal Gupta! I'll be out of camp a little while.

Muldoon, do not be telling me these things! I am not wishing to know!

Huh—oh, it's you, sir! Are you waiting for a driver?

Yes, Muldoon, I am waiting for you to drive me to that meeting you arranged with the Sikhs!

Sir, you wouldn't be interested in a game of snakes and ladders!

No, Muldoon, but I am interested in joining the patrol I heard you discuss! So drive on!

Sir, you ain't supposed to do this sort of thing! You're a doctor!

I am also Gurkha, Muldoon! We are warriors and in my own village I am looked on with less respect than the most humble soldier!

The patrol was ready to move out . . .

Lieutenant Ishar Singh, my Captain wants to come along as first-aid man.

My chaps won't object— as long as he leaves his castor-oil bottle behind!

Tiddim Tojo patrol going out!

Pass, friends!

The patrol probed forward . . .

These Sikhs laughed at me, Muldoon! I must teach them a Gurkha is not to be laughed at!

Yessir. Careful of the pothole, sir!

That's the one I was talking about, sir!

The lieutenant agrees with my notion that the Tiddim Tojo spotter is up on this hill. It overlooks every place that's being shelled!

Suddenly there was light . . .

A flare! They've rumbled us!

The machine-gun resumed firing . . .

The Sikhs are drawing fire. Now's our chance to get back.

Not at all, Muldoon! It's our chance to go forward!

Charge—argh!

There he goes again! The Light Brigade wouldn't have got far with this bloke leading 'em.

Muldoon took over . . .

Just keep hanging onto my belt, sir.

Thank you, Muldon! My spectacles tend to mist over in this humidity.

That cave must be Tiddim Tojo's spotter post.

There it is!

Wait while I wipe my spectacles!

Now I charge.

Wait till I've tossed in a couple of grenades, sir.

Muldoon pitched two grenades . . .

59

Major Parkin did his lecturing behind the cookhouse . . .

THE END

61

HANDSOME HARRY

HARRY HANSOM was a handsome young heavyweight nobody had heard of until his manager, Bert Fitch, arranged a contract for him to advertise 'Wham' after-shave lotion.

The firm wanted a well-known boxer, so Harry had to keep winning—and preserve his good looks!

ANOTHER FIVE MILES, HARRY. YOU'VE GOT TO BE IN SHAPE FOR YOUR FIGHT WITH MICK DERMOT.

RIGHT, BERT. I ENJOY TRAINING ANYWAY.

HEY, WATCH OUT FOR THAT FOOTBALL, HARRY!

URGH!

YOU ALL RIGHT, BERT? WHAT DID YOU DO THAT FOR?

OOH, ME HEAD'S RINGING! BUT IT'S WORTH IT, HARRY! CAN'T RISK GETTING YOUR LOOKS SPOILT!

But, a little later . . .

A MODEL PLANE! LOOK OUT, HARRY! DON'T GET THE PROPELLER IN YOUR FACE!

IT'S COMING BACK!

But as Bert went bustling in, advertising agent Max Baxter came bustling out!

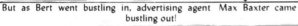

The End

RED STAR ROBINSON

Communication failure, Master Tom.

THE stormlashed crag of Rockall—secret base of Tom Robinson and Mr Syrius Thrice, the cultured robot, those tireless helpers of the Watcher, that mysterious being who guards the Earth's quadrant of space . . .

Grrtic . . . excessive sunspot activity . . . krrtrrk . . . worldwide disruption . . . grrrt . . .

No imput even on the Watcher's sealed beam. Master Tom, I deduce more of a problem than just a burst of sunspots.

That sounds serious, Mr Thrice! You mean . . .

A fault in our re-transmission satellite, Master Tom. We must investigate at once.

Mr Thrice, why can't I drive the Red Star limousine?

That would be most irregular, Master Tom. You do not even hold a road vehicle licence.

Now we beam in on the satellite's homing beacon.

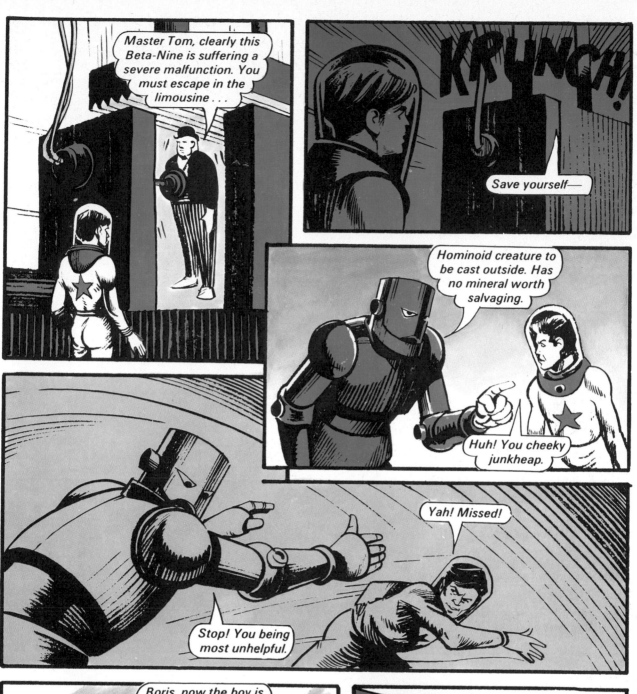

Tom drove off . . .

Wonder what would happen if that console got busted.

CRASH!

There it is. Seatbelt on—brace for collision . . .

Tom rammed the control console . . .

WHAM!

My thanks, Master Tom.

Mr Thrice! You're free.

Mr Thrice confronted the Beta-Nine . . .

I command you deactivate yourself.

Request declined. Must dispose of you and resume work.

71

THE PROFESSIONAL TOUCH

KINSLEY AMATEURS, a top-class amateur side were attracting the attention of the senior club scouts. Nick Moor's club, Barnley Rovers, rebuilding their side and currently struggling at the foot of the English First Division, were interested in the Kinsley goalkeeper, Dick Dorkin. But so too were Manston City, one of the top glamour clubs!

That was a powerful shot. Dorkin took it with ease.

Not a bad one-handed save!

Yeah! But he had all the time in the world to see it coming.

Suddenly, the opposing centre broke through, and—

In like a real amateur— head first! Too risky!

Those Manston City boys are hard! The lad has courage as well as skill!

As the Kinsley goal came under pressure—

He's not so clever in a tight situation!

Right through his legs! A sucker goal!

Dorkin failed to anticipate that shot!

The halftime whistle blew . . .

You'll have to look elsewhere for a keeper, Nick.

He certainly is a bit raw yet.

We're staying to watch the Kinsley strikers.

In the second half.

Dorkin's slow off the mark but he gets to the ball very quickly. He hasn't fumbled a ball in the worst possible conditions.

After the game, with Kinsley having won 5-1, the scouts gather round the strikers.

We're from Manston City—and—

I'd give anything to play for Manston. If only I hadn't let in that silly goal.

I'm Nick Moor, scout for Barnley Rovers. If you want to be a professional player, meet me at seven o'clock tomorrow night at this address.

What—yes, I'll be there!

Next night, at the Barnley Sports Centre . . . .

This is Dan Wellens, the best goalkeeper Barnley ever had. He's going to sharpen you up over the next few weeks.

Dan Wellens. Gee! I never thought I'd get to meet a famous Internationalist.

If Nick Moor thinks you have ability lad, you could be an internationalist yourself some day.

Later, Dick played in an indoor practice game.

That left hand is weak. Trust Nick to spot it!

Next night, Dick had an unusual training session.

Watch the ball, Dick! Try to anticipate the angle!

The following week, yet a new game for Dick—junior amateur ice-hockey!

That was a cracking save. Maybe we saw the boy on a bad day last time.

Dorkin had one great save after another . . .

Ooooh! Terrific save!

Dan Wellens really has improved Dorkin. His reflexes are razor sharp now!

This keeper is hot stuff! We'll have to sign him!

Thanks to Dorkin, Kinsley hung on to their one goal lead to lift the cup . . .

We've got to get Dorkin's signature! He's really something!

After the game . . .

We're from Manston City, Dick. We're interested in signing you up for City.

Sorry, you're too late! I signed for Barnley Rovers, just before the kick off!

How did you persuade him to sign for Barnley Rovers, Nick? He could have been a City star!

Oh, I just promised him that he could keep on playing basketball! He enjoys the game too much now to give it up. He always had the talent. All he needed was the professional touch!

IT'S A FUNNY OLD WORLD

ALL TIED UP
A mistle thrush was rescued by firemen recently after it had tangled itself up in the cotton it was using to build its nest with.

COOKING FOR CROOKS
The food in the police cells in the Guildhall in Nottingham is so good, one prisoner, on the day of his release, asked to stay until after dinner.

MARATHON MOGGIE
Ginger the tom-cat, walked 150 miles to return to his old home, from Anglesey in North Wales to his old farm in Loughborough, Leics. It took him 14 months.

MIS-DIRECTED MUTT
The world's worst mountain rescue dog, Bruno, has been sent out on eight missions in the past two years —and has succeeded in getting lost on every occasion.

WONDER WORM
There is now an aerosol which sprays "instant worms" The can squirts a long thread which looks like a real worm. There are several different "flavours" and they are proving popular as fishing bait.

TALL TREK.
Sylvian Dornon stilt-walked 1830 miles from Paris to Moscow in 1891.

WALL WALK
The authorities in Peking are very worried about the Great Wall of China. Peasants have been stealing lumps of it to build cowsheds, houses and pig sties. So far, 75 miles of wall have been taken.

STARHAWK

CENTURY 26 A.D.—and crime in space increased as the Terran Empire declined! The cargo ship Hermes was in trouble as an unknown force pulled it off course . . .

The tractor beam pulled the Hermes ever nearer, until.

At her lads. But be careful not to damage the merchandise. That's a valuable ship and cargo. Only the crew are of no use, and we know what to do with 'em! Eh?

Aye, Strafer. That we do!

It's dead! We've no power!

This one's an easy lock. The laser will be through it in seconds.

That's two big IF's, Stone and time is running out. They're breaking through!

The Communication systems are nearly drained of power, but if I can push what is left through in one surge and if this card means what they say it does . . .

RYNN CARD IF YOUR CAUSE BE JUST BUT THE ODDS ARE TOO GREAT, USE ME.

Moments later . . .

Go get 'em, lads!

You'll never get away with this piracy. Stand still or we'll . . .

CLICK!

I've two bits of bad news for you, boys. Firstly, your lasers are useless within the force beam we're pulling you in by . . .

That's him out of the game. Now let's see what's in here!

Rynn entered the huge craft, where . . .

Welcome, Sol Rynn. You have led my underlings a merry chase but now the game is at an end!

What in all the galaxy is this?

Some kind of hideous mu . . .

Yes, MUTANT, Rynn. I, Skaro, can reach into your mind.

You have cost me many men, Rynn. Men I need to perform the more physical tasks of this . . . er . . . salvage operation.

Piracy, more like!

DANGER HIGH ENERGY

I know every move you make against me even as you think of it! You stand no chance!

Aargh!

As Skaro advanced, Rynn fought to erect a mental barrier of random thoughts . . .

Only . . . way. Must erect a mind barrier . . .

You are resourceful, Rynn. But it is useless. Prepare to . . .

Die . . . can't . . . confound . . . Aaargh!

WILLIE THE WINNER

WILLIE WYNN had a knack of winning competitions...

Hey, look, Mum! I've won a trip to America in that Popsy Popcorn competition!

So Willie flew off to the good old U.S. of A. To a tearful farewell...

Bye, Willie... and don't forget to write...

...And a brassband welcome!

Now this is more like it. This is what I call a welcome!

We are proud to have you join us here at the Brassfoot Military Academy! If there's one thing we like in the States, it's a winner!

Well, you'll never see me losing!

Here are your sleeping quarters, and I suggest you get an early night, because tomorrow you start life as a soldier cadet to give you experience of how people in the States really live!

Thanks... sir! It sounds super! I think!

The first great sound was reveille ... at four-thirty a.m. ...

What's with all that noise in the middle of the night?

...Followed by the grating sound of the P.T. instructor's voice...

Hup, hup, hup!

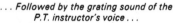

...And the sparkling tinkle of icy cold water...

Brrr... freezing cold shower! And we haven't had breakfast yet!

Breakfast was next . . .

Ugh! Cold porridge and toast! Maybe this wasn't the prize to win after all!

. . . And straight from the two course breakfast to the assault course . . .

Not exactly a holiday this . . .

. . . And I don't like it at all!

And, by the time he got up . . .

Where's everyone got to? Now I'm lost. And I'm not used to losing!

But Willie soon won his way back to civilisation . . .

I've been walking around for ages! Maybe that gate will lead back to the college.

But, as he stepped through . . .

What now? What's going on?

You are the millionth visitor to Wonderland! Welcome . . . You are our guest of honour and you have the freedom of the fairground for a day!

Who says you can't win 'em all? One thing's for sure! Winning sure beats losing!

The End.

CUSTER AND THE GUNPOWDER PLOT

"CUSTER speaking . . . So there I was, peace-loving old me, dodging Ye Glue Factorye by enlisting as war-horse of the dauntless Sir Waldo Twitch in that rumble with the Roundheads. One season, we found ourselves under siege in Nutebrook Manor . . ."

"A grim game was in hand among the boys . . ."

Gentlemen, lay your cards on the table!

Sir Waldo—my compliments. You win the last bite of food . . . the final saveloy.

Oddsblud! I'm overwhelmed!

Your aces certainly beat my knaves, Sir Waldo—hulloa! What is this in your sleeve?

SNATCH

More aces! Sir, you cheated. 'Twas I who won that sausage.

But—er, Sir Fitzbark—er, I know not how those cards came to my sleeve!

94

SPRING-HEELED JACK
(Continued from Page 38)

Pier six . . . Wednesday night. Ship . . . 'Lotus Rose' . . . they row the opium ashore . . . Let me down, guv!

You did well to tell! Now, you'll live!

Leave London tonight! Warn no one . . . or I'll find you.

I'll leave. They'd kill me if they found me!

Wednesday night . . .

Watch for the excise patrols.

We are safe in the fog . . .

But . . .

I must stop the opium but need to know where it was to be delivered . . .

There's bound to be an excise patrol around, somewhere.

Keeping to the rooftops, Jack followed the unsuspecting Chinaman who led him through a maze of side streets and dark, narrow alleys...

He'll need to tell his tong now the opium has been lost. But which Tong I wonder?

O Honourable Dragon, the poppy gold is destroyed. We were attacked. Then came the accursed men of the excise...

We strike! Our hatchets shall wipe out the insult.

Death to the Flame Tigers!

They head for Farthing Street! Then I know where the Temple of the Flame Tigers must be...

I can race them! I have to stop bloodshed... there'll be no tong war here.

100

Time to change back in a hurry. By this time, there will have been two arrests.

Later . . .

Take notes, Jackson! We've arrested the tong ring leaders. A lucky stroke.

Coming, Sergeant . . . .

Sergeant, we saw them put down by . . . er . . . by a leaping figure.

We think it was Spring-Heeled Jack.

Don't dare give me that Spring-Heeled Jack rubbish. It's a figment of your imagination. Jackson, ignore what these idiots just said. Only fools believe in Spring-Heeled Jack!

Whatever Sergeant Drew believes, the tong terror is over for a while. One thing's certain, the tongmen believe in Spring-Heeled Jack!

THE END

BERNARD BRIGGS the all-go goalie

BERNARD BRIGGS, top goalie and all-round sportsman, was delivering a 1929 De Witt Sueca to a buyer in Los Angeles, the profit to go to an orphanage. But the veteran car was heavy on petrol and Bernard was getting low on funds . . .

THAT LEAVES ME WITH JUST TEN DOLLARS. I'VE GOT TO FIND SOME MONEY FROM SOMEWHERE BEFORE I'VE USED THIS TANK OF GAS!

THESE CANS WOULD MAKE A NICE BIT OF ALUMINIUM SCRAP. I WONDER WHO COLLECTS THEM?

After visiting four more filling stations . . .

I SHOULD BE ABLE TO GET A FEW BUCKS FOR THESE CANS . . .

Bernard asked the filling-station owner.

THOSE CANS? THEY'RE JUST GARBAGE!

THEY MAY JUST BE GARBAGE TO YOU, MATE—BUT THEY'RE GOOD SCRAP. CAN I HAVE THEM?

But . . .

SOFT-DRINK CANS? CAN'T BE BOTHERED WITH THEM. THEY'RE JUST TRASH.

THEY'RE GOOD METAL AND THEY OUGHT TO BE RECLAIMED. I'LL FIND A REAL SCRAPMAN.

It was the same story at every scrapyard in Detroit . . .

LOOKS LIKE I'M STUCK WITH A CAR-FULL OF CANS NOBODY WANTS.

GOOD WORK, MAN! WELCOME ABOARD! THIS SPACESHIP NEEDS YOU!

'WELCOME ABOARD!' 'SPACE-SHIP'? WHAT DO YOU MEAN?

HERE WE ARE, MAN—SPACESHIP EARTH! WE SPECIALISE IN RE-CYCLING WASTE!

Spaceship Earth were pleased to get the cans—and pay for them . . .

LET ME SEE . . . WE OWE YOU TWELVE DOLLARS AND THIRTY-SEVEN CENTS!

NOT A BAD PRICE.

THIS IS A GOOD LINE. I CAN EARN SOME PETROL MONEY AND HELP THE ECOLOGY. BUT I'LL HAVE TO DO IT ON A LARGER SCALE.

I'LL HAVE A WORD WITH THE RINK-MANAGER HERE.

ICE HOCKEY TO-NITE
DETROIT HUB-CAPS
v
PITTSBURGH PUDDLERS

YOU WANT TO CLEAN THE STANDS FOR NOTHING? YOU MUST BE CRAZY! SURE, GO AHEAD.

RIGHT, MATE. IT'S A DEAL!

Bernard got to watch that night's game free . . .

HOCKEY. THAT'S A GIRLS' GAME.

But Bernard's ideas soon changed . . .

MAYBE IT'S TOUGHER THAN IT LOOKS . . .

YIKES! I DIDN'T EVEN SEE THAT GOAL!

The game ended in a 1-0 victory for the Hubcaps.

TIME TO GET TO WORK NOW.

PLAYERS

THERE MUST'VE BEEN AT LEAST TWELVE THOUSAND SPECTATORS, AND EVERY ONE OF THEM SEEMS TO HAVE HAD AT LEAST ONE DRINK. THAT'LL MAKE A FAIR BIT OF SCRAP.

While Bernard was working, the Hubcaps "B" team came out to practice.

THAT GUY LOOKS FAMILIAR . . .

HEY! AREN'T YOU BERNARD BRIGGS? YOU'RE A FAMOUS SOCCER PLAYER IN ENGLAND.

THAT'S THE NAME, MATE . . .

Next day . . .

I picked up this load at the Detroit Blockbusters' baseball stadium. It took me all morning but it didn't half tidy the place up and it should be worth a few bucks!

Far out, man! A few more guys like you, and we wouldn't need to worry about the ecology.

HEY—YOU BRIGGS?

THAT'S THE NAME, MATE. ANYTHING I CAN DO FOR YOU?

I'M SHELLEY FARBER, HUBCAPS' MANAGER. THE BOYS TOLD ME HOW WELL YOU DID IN THAT WORK-OUT THE OTHER NIGHT. WOULD YOU LIKE A GAME ON SATURDAY?

I DON'T MIND IF I DO, MATE—I'VE ALWAYS TIME FOR A BIT OF SPORT.

Bernard had rented a garage to store the De Witt-Sueca during his stay in Detroit.

THAT'S MY GARAGE— HEY!

THEY'VE GIVEN ME THE SLIP!

THEY TRIED TO FORCE THE LOCK. I'LL HAVE TO RIG UP SOME BETTER PROTECTION FOR THE CAR.

Bernard set to work.

THAT SHOULD TAKE CARE OF IT.

On Saturday . . .

YOU'D BETTER PUT ON SOME PADDING, BERNARD.

NO THANKS, MATE. ALL THAT STUFF WOULD SLOW ME DOWN.

106

The Hubcaps were playing the Richmond Rangers.

As Bernard made to help the opponent to his feet . . .

The thrown punch was the signal for an all-out brawl.

Three of the offenders were sent off for two minutes.

NOW WE HAVE A ONE-MAN ADVANTAGE FOR TWO MINUTES. THIS IS CALLED A "POWER PLAY".

I'M UNMARKED.

IT'S IN THE NET!

YOU PLAYED A BLINDER, BERNARD. YOU'LL SOON BE OUR TOP ATTRACTION.

I'M STILL JUST GETTING THE HANG OF IT, MATE.

BERNARD MY BOY! YOU WERE GREAT! I'VE GOT A CONTRACT MADE OUT

SORRY, MR FARBER. I'VE GOT A CAR TO DELIVER. I'LL TURN OUT FOR YOU WHILE I'M IN DETROIT, BUT NO CONTRACT.

Back at Bernard's garage . . .

UH-HUH! LOOKS LIKE MY VISITORS CAME BACK—AND THIS TIME THEY GOT IN!

Bernard had fixed up weighted socks to hit any intruder on the head!

MY LITTLE WELCOMER WORKED. I WONDER WHO THESE TWO BIRDS ARE? I'LL CALL THE COPS.

LOOKS LIKE YOU'VE GOT TROUBLE, MISTER. THAT'S BIG AL CINTRA AND JOE ABALONE—TWO MAFIA HOODS.

MAFIA?

THE MAFIA? WHAT COULD THE MAFIA WANT WITH ME?

A week later . . .

TOO SLOW, MATE!

THAT'S OUR FIFTH—AND MY HAT-TRICK! THAT SHOULD GIVE US THE GAME.

The Hubcaps won 5-1.

THIS MAKES YOU THE TEAM'S TOP SCORER SINCE YOU JOINED, BERNARD.

IT'S THE TEAM, AL. THEY'RE PLAYING TOGETHER WELL.

After the match, the star of the rink had another task.

THERE MUST BE A BETTER WAY OF ORGANIZING THIS CAN COLLECTING— IF ONLY I CAN THINK OF IT!

Bernard sold his cans to an ecology group calling themselves "The Crew of Space Ship Earth".

THIS LOAD SHOULD KEEP ME IN HAMBURGER MONEY FOR A FEW DAYS.

HEY! WHAT IS THIS?

PUBLICITY, MAN! NOW YOU'RE A HOCKEY STAR THIS'LL REALLY GIVE ECOLOGY IN DETROIT A BOOST!

But the publicity was not so welcome to Shelly Farber, manager of the Hubcaps.

YOU DON'T NEED TO DO THIS, BERNIE BOY! WE'D PAY YOU A FAT SALARY IF ONLY YOU'D ACCEPT IT! THIS HARMS THE CLUB'S IMAGE!

I AIN'T ASHAMED OF BEING A SCRAP-MAN, MR FARBER. BUT DON'T WORRY. I'LL COME UP WITH SOMETHING THAT'LL KEEP US BOTH HAPPY.

The Hubcaps' next game was home to the Boston Brahmins, the league-leaders and top-scorers.

HEY, I BET THAT'LL BE A GREAT GAME!

YEAH—BUT WE DON'T HAVE TWO BUCKS EACH. FORGET IT!

THAT GIVES ME AN IDEA...

TODAY HUBCAPS v BOSTON BRAHMINS

SAY, KIDS, WOULD YOU LIKE FREE TICKETS FOR THE MATCH?

TODAY HUBCAPS v BOSTON BRAHMINS

YOU BET—BUT WHERE'S THE CATCH?

That evening...

I TOLD YOU YOU'D SOON BE A STAR ATTRACTION, BERNARD!

BRIGGS IS GREAT

HUBCAPS BRIGGS

BRIGGS BRIGGS

YEAH, AL, BUT THE BRAHMINS ARE THE BEST TEAM I'VE FACED YET!

The game got under way.

THEY WEREN'T EXPECTING A QUICK BREAK.

Later.

UNNNH!

COME ON, BERNARD! PITCH IN!

NOT ME, MATE. I'M HERE TO PLAY ICE-HOCKEY—NOT JOIN IN A FREE-FOR-ALL.

When the referees eventually restored order....

LOOKS LIKE ED'S OUT FOR THE DURATION, FELLAS, AND THE RESERVE IS INJURED. WHO'LL GO IN GOAL?

I'LL GIVE IT A TRY, AL. IT SHOULD BE EASY MINDING A NET THAT SMALL.

NO THANKS, AL. I DON'T WANT TO LOOK LIKE THE MAN IN THE IRON MASK. I'M UGLY ENOUGH AS IT IS!

THE GOAL'S SMALL, BUT SO'S THE PUCK! AND IT GETS A MOVE ON, TOO!

Outside the rink . . .

SEE, I TOLD YA. THAT LIMEY IS A SUCKER IF HE THINKS WE'D STICK AROUND TO HELP HIM CLEAN UP THEM CRUMMY STANDS.

I THOUGHT I MIGHT FIND YOU HERE. COME ON — YOU'VE GOT WORK TO DO!

WE WEREN'T GOING NOWHERE, MISTER — HONEST. JUST STEPPED OUT FOR A BREATH OF AIR.

YOU KIDS ARE DAFT, SNEAKING OFF LIKE THAT. IF YOU GOT YOURSELVES ORGANISED, YOU COULD SEE ALL THE SPORTS EVENTS IN DETROIT FREE!

SAY, HE'S GOT SOMETHING! IMAGINE WATCHING THE TIGERS FOR JUST AN HOUR OR SO'S WORK!

MR BRIGGS?

YEAH, MATE?

I THINK I CAN SEE MY WAY CLEAR TO OFFERING YOU A CONTRACT WITH THE BRAHMINS WORTH 500,000 DOLLARS.

HALF A MILLION BUCKS! STONE THE CROWS!

HANG ON THERE! I'VE JUST COME FROM A BOARD-MEETING AND I CAN TOP THAT OFFER BY 250,000 DOLLARS!

I THINK, WITH MY BOARD'S APPROVAL, I COULD GO AS HIGH AS A MILLION—

SORRY, MATES. I DON'T TAKE MONEY FOR MY SPORT! BESIDES, I'VE ALREADY GOT A JOB—DELIVERING A CAR!

Bernard had earned enough from collecting cans to move on.

IT'S GREAT, THE WAY YOU GOT THE KIDS ORGANIZED, MAN! THEY'RE EARNING BREAD AND HELPING THE ECOLOGY TOO!

JUST KEEP 'EM AT IT, MATE. MAYBE I'LL BE IN TOUCH WITH ANOTHER BRANCH OF YOUR ORGANIZATION SOMETIME.

With just 200 dollars in his pocket, Bernard set out for Chicago.

CHICAGO

THAT'S THE FIRST TIME I'VE EVER TURNED DOWN AN OFFER OF A MILLION DOLLARS. THIS IS SOME COUNTRY!

The End.

KING COBRA

BILL KING, a world-wide free-lance reporter, was in the old Arab city of Kashram. Clive Lane, the famous film director, was making a picture "The Flame of the East," a multi-million dollar epic which was obviously going to be a world-beater. Competition for the director post had been terrific and Bill knew there was a great newspaper story in it . . .

Right! Action! Cameras!

H

This is where the native population strikes back on their oppressors, King. These blocks of stone are made of plastic, of course—

It looks very realistic to me. The action is terrific!

It's all very well done and—hey—that block of stone can't be plastic! Look at the effort that man is—Lane!

Mr Lane, can I ask you if—

What? Look out—!

What—! That's a real rock. How—?

Lane's safe and there goes the killer. I must get hold of him—

Bill King was King Cobra, the amazing crook catcher. He'd been tipped off that a contract had been put out on Lane's life. His reporter cover enabled him to keep an eye on Lane. Quickly, he changed into his King Cobra outfit and went after the killer . . .

115

That's the most amazing trick photography, Clive. It looks absolutely real.

That's because it IS real. No tricks, Bill. My technicians have built genuine flying carpets for me, jet-propelled.

Oh, no! An aircraft. This is all supposed to be happening centuries ago. We'll have to re-shoot that scene tomorrow.

I'd like to be allowed to watch the re-take, Clive. Can you show me how these carpets are controlled?

Sure thing, Bill. Let's hope it's not so dangerous as the street scene, eh!

The following morning . . .

The controls are simple, Bill, and they are masked by the carpet's fringe which blows back in flight.

Anyone can fly it, Bill. Now where are the actors for this re-shooting?

In a room below, the actors were making up for their parts when—

Hey! You can't come— what's going on?

Shut up. Everyone against the wall.

Bill King was right, someone else had got Mollin's job.

Up to the roof. Keep your guns out of sight until we're ready to make our move.

Okay, Dingo! You're the boss!

117

119

The Legend of Spirit Crossing

IN 1862, a United States Army supply waggon train, commanded by Captain Tim Weaver, was travelling through the Badlands of New Mexico on the way to Fort Bent. For the last ten miles, every move of the column had been watched by the hostile Chiricahua Apaches . . .

The Bluecoat wagons are heavily laden. The supplies they carry will arm our warriors and bring much comfort to our people.

The Bluecoats will stop at Spirit Crossing. We will fight them on the sacred ground of our ancestors.

121

A Ghost Dancer! He is pledged to fight to the death!

Arrgh!

BANG

Keep down, men. Douse the flames! The firelight is making us clear targets!

I hit him, Captain.

He's gone! Vanished into thin air! We are fighting ghosts!

No sign of them so far. They must be hiding near the top! Four of us will climb up— the rest stay here!

Those bats are the only living things we've seen!

It's weird, Captain. I'm beginning to think the stories about this place could be true.

Look! Another Ghost Dancer. Where did he come from?

That is one dead Apache!

He's gone! Vanished! Like a ghost!

Ghosts don't bleed! That trail will lead us to him!

WHEEE... EEEEEE

A tunnel! So that is how they do it!

WHEEE... EEE.

There are your ghosts, men, getting ready for another attack! We'll charge them!

The Ghost Dancers stood no chance and the action was short and sharp.

That takes care of the Ghost Dancers. We won't hear any more spirit voices now.

Later— **WHEEEE-EEEE**

The spirit voices again, Captain? What's going on?

There must be some natural explanation. Probably a trick of wind, but we must find out before the men panic—

There! A bat. But one bat couldn't make the racket we heard. We'll check in daylight.

At dawn . . . It is strange. We've been all through the tunnel and there's no sign of any bats. They must be somewhere—

Hey, look out! Get away. Bats ugh!

The men have found them! They are your spirit voices, Sergeant! The Apaches must think their dead warriors become bats!

The soldiers dug out the soft sand and opened an entrance to a huge cavern . . .

A natural echo chamber. The main entrance must have silted up leaving that crack as the only way in. The noise the bats make coming and going are amplified by the cavern and funneled out through that small crack just above our positions.

WHEEE

WHEEE

WHEEEEE

A sentry's call summoned Weaver . . .

Apaches, Captain! Hundreds of them!

What are they waiting for, Captain.

It's a war of nerves. They will wait until the setting sun is shining into our eyes. Come on, we've got a lot to do—

Weaver issued orders, which puzzled Sergeant Hadley . . .

We'll play the Apaches at their own game, Sergeant. Put thatch up on the roof, make some uniformed dummies, and have some men with shovels follow me.

Y . . . yes, sir. Thatch the roof! Make dummy soldiers! Men with shovels!

Wonder why the Captain wants us to make a flute for every man.

Search me, Kelly! In this man's army, you just do what you're told!

The Apaches are waiting to attack and the Captain has us digging tunnels and thatching roofs. What gives?

The Captain knows what he's doing! I hope—

Towards sunset, the attack began.

Don't let the bats spook you, men!

It ain't the bats I'm worried about, Captain. Them Indians aim to burn us out!

The spirits of our dead warriors call out to us! Death to the Bluecoats!

Don't panic, men. Stick to your orders. Get inside the Mission.

We have them trapped. Kill the Bluecoat captain.